Rich Pickings

With best wishes
Oliver Preston

Rich Pickings

Oliver Preston

BEVERSTON PRESS

For Amber and Rex

First published in Great Britain in 2013 by

BEVERSTON PRESS

Tetbury, Glos GL8 8TT

Copyright © 2013 Oliver Preston

The right of Oliver Preston to be identified as the author of this work has been
asserted to him in accordance with the Copyright, Designs and Patents Act 1988.

The author and publisher has made every reasonable effort to contact all copyright holders.
Any errors that may have occurred are inadvertent and anyone who for any reason has not
been contacted is invited to write to the publishers so that a full acknowledgement
may be made in subsequent editions.

British Library cataloguing in Publication Data
A catalogue record for this title is available from The British Library

ISBN 978 0 9549936 5 8

Designed by boinggraphics.co.uk
Printed by Gutenberg Press, Malta

"Well, here's to GIVING UP giving things up."

INTRODUCTION

I recently found an old desk diary from my City days, and looked up the 26th October 1995, the day that I had quit banking to become a cartoonist. It was one of those big corporate diaries, with weekly contemplatory quotes at the top of each page. I was immediately struck by how the quotations seemed almost tailor-made for me as I questioned whether I was really doing the right thing: *"The secret of happiness is not in doing what one likes, but in liking what one has to do"*(James M Barrie); *"If your heart is not clear, the day will be foggy."*(Russian proverb); *"Laughter is the closest distance between two people."*(Victor Borge); and, *"There are two mistakes one can make along the road to truth: not going all the way, and not starting."*(Buddha). It's funny to look back at it now, but it was such a dramatic change of direction for me personally, and it seems very bizarre with hindsight how I was getting reassurance from the most unlikely of sources.

"Rich Pickings", is my twelfth book of cartoons and illustrations, and I cannot believe that I am still lucky enough to be able to make a living from doing what I love - observing what goes on around me, and turning those observations into cartoons. Starting with a blank piece of paper and a pencil, and then using a pen and India ink to firm up my ideas. Then the lavish colouring with inks and gouache, what my wife calls, 'painting by numbers'. The results can be very wayward: A tethered goat turbo grazing a garden, iPads at the bottom of pools, fox hunting in the Facebook age, and garrulous grandees and bridge playing dames all feature in this anthology of my cartoons. I now have small children, who are great at helping me see the funny side of things, and now my work takes me around the United Kingdom (and Europe) where I get to observe wonderful idiosyncrasies, and the vagaries of modern life, which often will be later turned into cartoons. I watch and see everything, and take note of people's clothes and expressions, and a wry turn of phrase or side swiping comment very often becomes the caption for one of my next drawings. As one gets get older, I for one get happier, and I appreciate the variety of work that every day brings for me - for magazines and newspapers, caricatures and getting out on the farm here in the Cotswolds.

You will be reassured that I do now have public liability insurance for my cartooning, which is fortunate, because at a recent fair one of my greeting card stands was toppled sideways by a sharp gust of wind. It nearly flattened an old lady. Just imagine, she could have died laughing at one of my jokes (I wish.) Recently at Scone Palace in Perthshire, attending the Scottish Game Fair, a tweeded Scot came up to me and said, "You obviously know the same people as I do, "he went on, "all my friends are in your cartoons."

I do like the last quote of 1995 in the old Lehman Brothers diary, which seems quite apt for me now, as I have recently turned 50. It is by that great writer and wit - Brigitte Bardot. She says, *"It is sad to grow old but nice to ripen."* I hope the same happens with my cartooning.

OLIVER PRESTON.

"Panic Over. We've found our glasses."

OLIVER PRESTON.

"*You should have married that Prince William while you had the chance.*"

"Do look Philip. It's the fly past."

"Polo - The Harry Hunters."

"Dear mummy, 2 day I got X pelled."

"But mummy, a helpless poor creature has to suffer so I can have this..."

"Don't worry darling, your father won't get the bill for a couple of weeks."

"*Well, at least we can afford the heating this year.*"

"I hope there's more to your retirement than just organising my life."

"The Post Mortem"

"I never knew Bridge was so dangerous. Last week it was Colonel Mustard in the dining room with the lead piping."

"Have you seen the queue for the lift?
We MAY have to ski down."

"..and what exactly was it that attracted you to your billionaire husband?"

"*Ah yes, that's my husband. I recognise my shopping.*"

"*I now understand why she needs TWO fur coats.*"

"Darling, there's something I need to tell you."

Gstaad
"The annual test for visitors in pronouncing the name of the village."

"..and can you tell your father that the government has changed its mind about the mansion tax?"

"You know, I've got eyes in the back of my head."

"I'll steer. You do the gears."

"We had a few too many drinks so we decided to take a bus home."

"Mummy can't be bothered to get up, so we drive ourselves to school."

"What am I up to?
Nothing much, just a quiet night in with the girls."

OLIVER PRESTON

*"I've chucked out everything up to 2006.
They were way past their sell-by-date."*

"I think you're a little bit out of our league.
Maybe you should try our Chelsea meetings."

"and please, please, PLEASE get well soon."

"Polo - The returning Argie"

OLIVER PRESTON.

"How did the, 'I want you all to take a pay cut or leave'
strategy go down?"

"..and when I open my eyes,
the ipad's going to be back where I left it."

*"I didn't say my wife had played at Wimbledon.
I said she'd been to Wimbledon."*

"It's all Greek to me."

"Come on dad, it's only a toy."

"Coo-ee ! We're ready for your pièce de resistance."

OLIVER PRESTON

"Very nice, but the house needs to go a bit to the right."

"My plants are committing suicide."

"What an amazing coincidence it's a taxi company.
Would anyone like a cab home?"

"The Finesse"

"This is nothing. You should see her playing Bridge."

*"Granny, do you call us all darling
because you can't remember our names?"*

"I tell you, it's a dog eat dog world out there."

"What's wrong with me becoming
more and more like my mother every day?"

"You're speaking to the head of sales. Can I help?"

"Why don't you just GIVE UP. You've been at it all day,
and frankly, some of us are trying to get some sleep."

"...and after all that, did you actually land the fish?"

"This is about as much fun as watching you play cricket."

"...and don't all cheer if I hit one."

"It was much more fun when you were shooting."

"Bomb-a-diers."

"Whose bright idea was it to go round the house turning off lights?"

OLIVER PRESTON

"I give in. Give me a clue."

"*The trouble with Facebook is that everyone knows where you are.*"

"*Did anyone see where that went?*"

"There it is again, that funny rattling noise.
You really should take the car in and get it fixed."

"..and thank you, Lord, that I'm not a cat."

*"David, this is your mother speaking.
Come down from up there RIGHT NOW."*

"..and this was the landing..."

OLIVER PRESTON.

"Bringing
Christmas
on"

OLIVER PRESTON.

*"I don't know why you're looking so smug.
It's at your house next year."*

"Rudolph's big entrance"

OLIVER PRESTON

ACKNOWLEDGEMENTS

Illustration Acknowledgements
First published
9,11,13,15,22,23,24,25,33,35,36,39,45,47,52,53,55,61,63,67,68,69,70,71,73,76,78,80,81,83, 93
The Field Magazine; 12,42,43 *The Polo Magazine;* 21, 29 *Gstaad My Love Magazine.*

By the same author

Liquid Limericks (2001)	Robson Books	with Alistair Sampson
Larder Limericks (2004)	Robson Books	with Alistair Sampson
Shall we join the Men (2005)	Beverston Press	
Modern Cautionary Verses (2006)	Constable Robinson	with Charlie Ottley
Hitting the Slopes (2008)	Beverston Press	
How to be Asked Again (2009)	Quiller	with Rosie Nickerson
Out of Town (2010)	Beverston Press	
Out for a Duck (2010)	Quiller	with Ian Valentine
Another Log on the Fire (2011)	Beverston Press	
Real Men Drink Port (2011)	Quiller	with Ben Howkins
Fondue and Furs (2011)	Beverston Press	

My thanks to Simon Russell at Boing for the design and layout preparation, and Bobby Blackstock at The Gutenberg Press, Malta, for printing and advice. Thank you to Jill Schumm and Catherine Beale at Beverston Press, and Jonathan Young, editor, and Rebecca Hawtrey Art Editor at The Field Magazine and Richenda Hines, editor The Polo Magazine and The Racing Magazine. To Elsbeth Preston, Vivien, Amber and Rex, and Baloo, for such a wonderful source of ideas.

Prints and greeting cards are available from *'Rich Pickings'*
Visit www.beverstonpress.com or call +44 (0) 1666 502638